...and the Blood Flowed Green

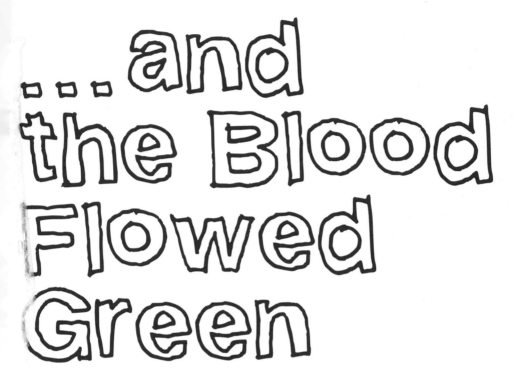

ALAN NOLAN

THE O'BRIEN PRESS
DUBLIN

For Lizzie Bun

First published 2012 by The O'Brien Press Limited
12 Terenure Road East, Rathgar, Dublin 6, Ireland
Tel: +353 1 492 3333; Fax: +353 1 492 2777
Email: books@obrien.ie
Website: www.obrien.ie

ISBN: 978-1-84717-257-0

British Library Cataloguing-in-Publication Data
A Catalogue record for this title is available from the British Library

1 2 3 4 5 6 7
12 13 14 15 16

The O'Brien Press receives assistance from

Printed and bound by CPI Group (UK) Ltd, Croydon, CR0 4YY
The paper used in this book is produced using pulp from managed forests

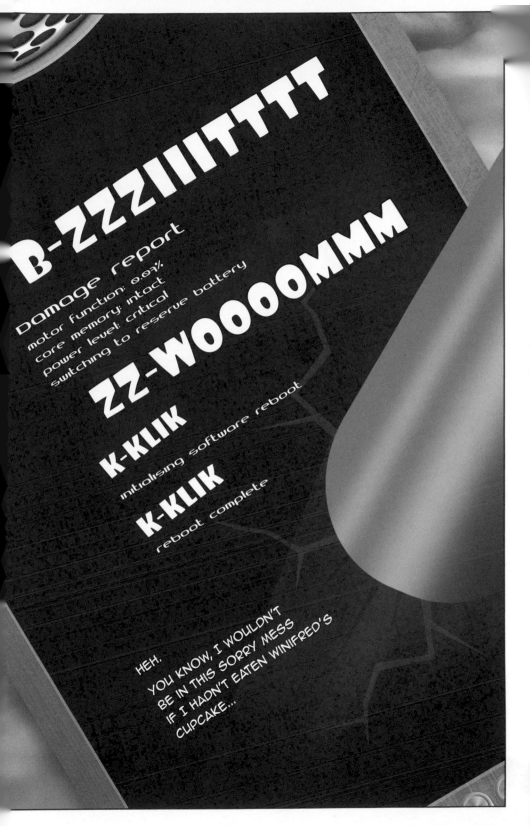

B-ZZZIIITTTT

damage report
motor function: 0.03%
core memory: intact
power level: critical
switching to reserve battery

ZZ-WOOOOMMM

K-KLIK

initialising software reboot

K-KLIK

reboot complete

HEH,
YOU KNOW, I WOULDN'T
BE IN THIS SORRY MESS
IF I HADN'T EATEN WINIFRED'S
CUPCAKE...

I'D BEEN SEEING WINNIE FOR A FEW MONTHS AND SHE WAS ALWAYS ENTERING BAKING COMPETITIONS.

IN FAIRNESS, I THOUGHT SHE'D MADE THE CUPCAKE FOR ME.

IT WAS DECORATED WITH STARS AND HAD A LITTLE SPACESHIP ON IT. THAT'S WHAT I DO, YOU SEE.

NO, I'M NOT AN ASTRONAUT. WELL, NOT THEN ANYWAY.

I WRITE SCIENCE FICTION BOOKS.

WELL, I'VE WRITTEN *ONE* SCIENCE FICTION BOOK – *'MILKY WAY MEMOIRS'*. HAVE YOU READ IT?

THOUGHT NOT. NO MANY PEOPLE DID

IT'S THE STORY OF A LOST SPACEMAN TRYING TO FIND HIS WAY BACK TO EARTH. PRETTY *IRONIC* GIVEN MY CURRENT PREDICAMENT.

I'M STILL WORKING ON THE FOLLOW UP.

EIGHT YEARS LATER...

YOU SEE, I HAD THIS *ONE* BOOK IN ME, AND THEN MY INSPIRATION SORT OF...

...DRIED UP.

A BIT LIKE MY RELATIONSHIP WITH WINNIE.

GROMPH

GET OUT!

SEEMS THE CUPCAKE WASN'T FOR ME AFTER ALL.

YOU SELFISH, LAZY, BONE-IDLE, DIRTY-LOOKIN' *EEJIT*. MY MA WAS RIGHT ABOUT YOU! *GET OUT!*

AND THAT'S HOW I FOUND MYSELF HERE.

THE ALIENS WERE QUITE APOLOGETIC...

BUT THAT DIDN'T STOP THEM *MAROONING* ME ON THIS BACKWATER PLANET SEVENTY-FIVE LIGHT YEARS FROM EARTH WITH ONLY A TRANSLATOR ROBOT FOR COMPANY.

THAT'S HIMSELF THERE. MY VERY OWN *REMOTE UNIVERSAL TRANSLATOR.*

RUNT, I CALL HIM.

HE TRANSLATES ALL THE DIFFERENT ALIEN LANGUAGES DIRECTLY INTO MY HEAD USING SOME SORT OF ADVANCED ROBOT TELEPATHY.

WORKS FOR MY FRIENDS, TOO, WHICH IS GREAT

HE'S A BIT LIKE A *TRAVEL GUIDE* AS WELL, HAS LOADS OF FACTS AND FIGURES AND ALL THAT. HE'S QUITE HANDY TO HAVE, REALLY.

CAN'T UNDERSTAND A WORD *HE* SAYS, THOUGH.

00111001100010011111010111

SIGH

AND MYSELF? THE NAME'S MULLIGAN. *MARION MULLIGAN.*

DON'T ASK.

LET'S JUST SAY MY MA WAS A BIG *JOHN WAYNE* FAN AND COWBOY MOVIE FAN AND MY DA HAD A *FUNNY SENSE OF HUMOUR.*

MY FRIENDS CALL ME *MICK,* OR USUALLY JUST *MULLIGAN.*

BUT AROUND HERE, FRIENDS ARE IN *SHORT SUPPLY.*

Haven

Coordinates 13.156.479.22
4th planet in the Baker system
Class 3
Nitrogen/oxygen atmosphere

The planet of **Haven**, in the forgotten outer rim of the western spiral arm of the Milky Way Galaxy, was named after the being who discovered it, **Tremell Haven**, and was claimed in the name of his home planet Thanis.

Haven was an unoccupied planet with no indigenous population of its own and seemed ripe for exploitation by the resource-greedy Thanisians.

However, after some preliminary explorations which showed up no significant deposits of minerals or precious metals, the Thanisian Government determined that they didn't particularly want the new planet after all, and so Haven became a haven for many different races of transient alien lifeforms, most of whom are either down on their luck with no place else to go, or in trouble and on the run. Mostly barren desert, Haven boasts only one noteworthy township: the 'city' of **Flotsam**, and has no central government or law.

flotsam

Travel advice:
Don't bother, you really won't like it.

Grade:

SO THAT'S THE STORY, RORY.

STRANDED IN FLOTSAM CITY ON THE PLANET HAVEN.

AND IT WAS JUST AS MUCH OF A KIP AS *RUNT* SUGGESTED IT WOULD BE.

I GOT A JOB AS A BARMAN AT ONE OF THE *CANTINAS* ON FLOTSAM'S MAIN (AND ONLY) STREET.

THE PAY WAS LOUSY, THE HOURS WERE TERRIBLE AND THE CLIENTELE WAS DOG ROUGH.

I THINK THAT'S WHY I WORKED THERE. IT REMINDED ME OF *DUBLIN*.

HERE WE GO, FELLERS – SEVEN BUNYIPS. READ 'EM AND WEEP.

TROUBLE, MULLIGAN!

NO THANKS CRK, I'VE JU[ST] HAD SOME

IT'S ZEEBO, MULLY.

OF COURSE IT IS. WHAT'S HE DONE NOW?

SAME AS LAST TIME – HE'S LOST BIG ON THE BAMBAM RACING. CAN'T PAY. HE'S BEEN LOCKED UP.

GAMBLING AGAIN?? WHO'S GOT HIM THIS TIME?

BRINNER. I HEAR HE'S GOING TO MAKE AN EXAMPLE OF HIM.

AT DAWN, ZEEBO'S HISTORY!

BAD NEWS. THERE WAS NO LAW ON HAVEN, BUT BRINNER WASN'T ABOVE DISHING OUT HIS OWN BRAND OF JUSTICE.

HE WAS THE LOCAL WARLORD, A LOW RENT HOODLUM WITH HIS OWN PAID MILITIA. HE HAD A REPUTATION FOR SHOOTING FIRST, SHOOTING AGAIN, AND NOT BOTHERING WITH ASKING QUESTIONS LATER.

NOT THE KIND OF ALIEN YOU'D WANT TO INTRODUCE TO YOUR AUNTIE DOREEN.

NOT UNLESS YOU DIDN'T LIKE YOUR AUNTIE DOREEN.

OKAY, WE'D BETTER ROLL.

OH, HOW I WISH I COULD GET OFF THIS PLANET...

crk-tish-crrrkkk

Species: Azurian

Home Planet: Azur

Azurians are semi-amphibious beings, equally at home on land or in water, which is convenient as their home planet Azur is made from pure water.

Azurians breathe through hidden gills and communicate by whistling and clicking their "face fingers".

Crk is an atypical Azurian in that he has chosen to leave his home planet which is under constant attack by water pirates intent on stealing the precious liquid to sell to the highest bidders.

crk

zeebo obeez

Species: Skriiichan

Home Planet: Quilly's World

The forest planet of Quilly's World is home to two sentient races, the Skriiichans and their mortal enemies, the rodent-like Soorans.

Skriiichans are descended from birds, and retain vestigial feathers. Loud and boorish, Zeebo's race have a reputation for being petty thieves with a weakness for 'collecting' and hoarding shiny objects such as gemstones or coins.

a soorun

I GOT GILLY TO LOOK AFTER THE CANTINA AND HEADED OUT INTO THE BRUSH WITH CRK ON A COUPLE OF JUNKER BIKES FROM CRK'S BIKE SHOP. BRINNER'S COMPOUND WAS 12 KLIKS SOUTH OF FLOTSAM CITY.

CRK WAS A *COMPUTER GENIUS*, MADE FOR BETTER THINGS THAN FIXING UP JUNKER BIKES.

HE WANTED TO GET HOME JUST AS MUCH AS I DID.

14

planet hop®

The **Planet Hop®** travel system was developed in the early 17368s Central Galactic Era by **Grunt Newtgrabbler** the Telosian who also created the mind implant-based social network, Brainbook.

Planet Hop® is a matter transmitting service, with the capability of converting an object or a lifeform into an energy pattern which can then be 'beamed' over very large distances of space and reconverted into matter once it has reached its target destination.

With **Planet Hop®** space travel which previously would have taken months or even years can be achieved in an instant, with short hops from planet to planet using the Planet Hop® terminals.

Unfortunately for the budding space traveller in a rush, the **Planet Hop®** service is prohibitively expensive, as it uses the power of rare and valuable Doo-Han crystals as part of its technology.

Planet Hop® is an ultra-fast way to travel, but its price puts it out of reach of all but the ultra-rich.

IMPORTANT NOTE: DANGER OF DEATH!

A six-hour resting period between planet hops is strongly recommended. Failure to rest between hops can result in cellular degeneration and death.

mecha nova

Mecha Nova is the only planet in the Delta Quadrant of the galaxy which is populated almost entirely by sentient robots.

The planet has had a turbulent past, gifted, as it was, to robo-kind long ago by the now defunct Galactic Supreme Council as a homeworld for any robot who achieved sentience.

Mecha Nova's policy of allowing any and all robots access to their new homeworld led to many defunct and decommissioned war robots to make their way there, and this in turn led to decades of political instability and several civil wars and military robot coups.

Despite this, peace has reigned on Mecha Nova now for over twenty years and the planet's business now is robot production – robots are designed and built in vast robot factories tourism with Mecha Nova being visited by over 18 million tourists each year.

visit:

Robo Lake – a huge lake of molten metal, a by-product of the robo-factories.

eat at:

RoboJo's – a restaurant serving a selection of galactic dishes including Azurian snurk pie and a large range of Telosian curries.

Grade:

GAAAHHH! WE'RE IN A WAR ZONE!

IFEFORMS! THIS WAY!

IT IS NOT SAFE FOR YOU HERE!

MY DESIGNATION IS JINX-928.

WHO WERE THOSE GUYS?!

GENERAL PUGG'S MACHINES.

THEY ARE ROBO-SUPREMACISTS. THEY DESIRE TO HAVE MECHA NOVA EXCLUSIVELY FOR ROBO-KIND AND WISH DEATH TO ALL NON-ROBOTIC LIFEFORMS.

I AM PART OF A ROBO-RESISTANCE GROUP. WE HAVE NO QUARREL WITH ORGANIC BEINGS.

THE ONLY WAY MECHA NOVA CAN SURVIVE IN THIS GALAXY IS FOR ROBOT AND FLESH KIND TO WORK TOGETHER.

THIS IS A SAFE HOUSE, UNDER THE PROTECTION OF THE ROBO-RESISTANCE.

YOU MUST MEET THE OTHERS. THIS WAY.

KRIK-KLIK. KRIK-KLIK.

27

28

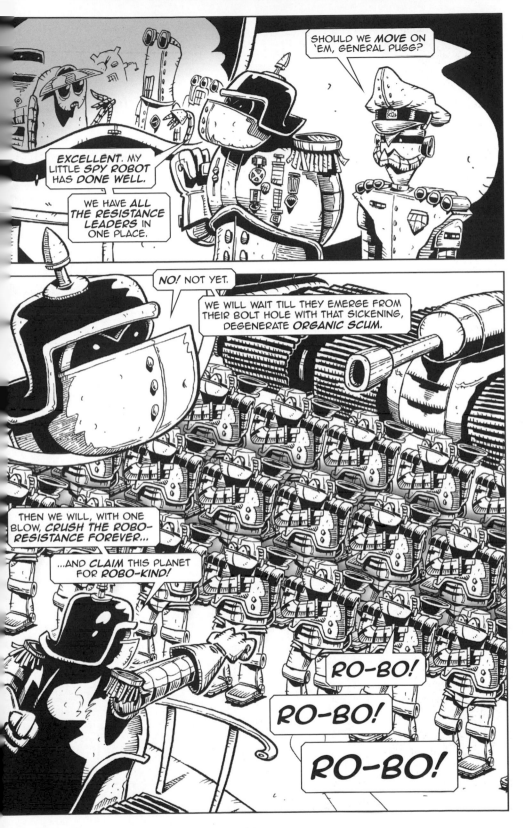

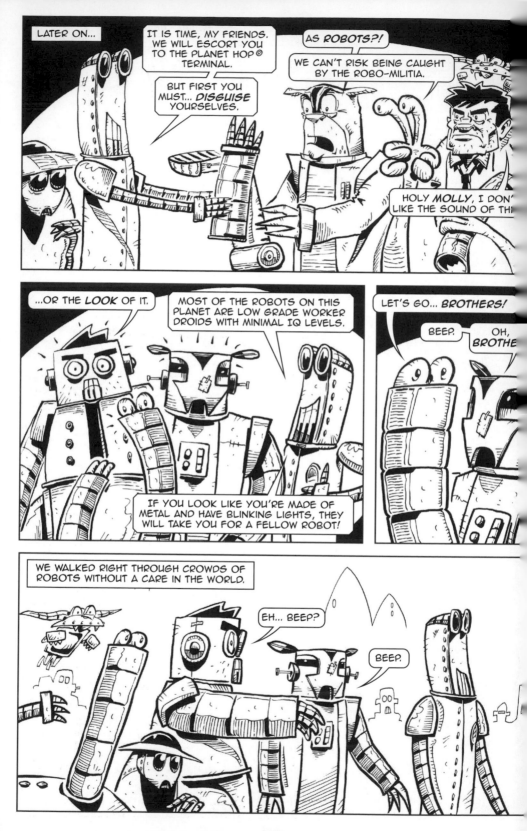

LATER ON...

IT IS TIME, MY FRIENDS. WE WILL ESCORT YOU TO THE PLANET HOP® TERMINAL.

BUT FIRST YOU MUST... *DISGUISE* YOURSELVES.

AS *ROBOTS?!*

WE CAN'T RISK BEING CAUGHT BY THE ROBO-MILITIA.

HOLY *MOLLY,* I DON'T LIKE THE SOUND OF THI...

...OR THE *LOOK* OF IT.

MOST OF THE ROBOTS ON THIS PLANET ARE LOW GRADE WORKER DROIDS WITH MINIMAL IQ LEVELS.

IF YOU LOOK LIKE YOU'RE MADE OF METAL AND HAVE BLINKING LIGHTS, THEY WILL TAKE YOU FOR A FELLOW ROBOT!

LET'S GO... *BROTHERS!*

BEEP.

OH, *BROTHE...*

WE WALKED RIGHT THROUGH CROWDS OF ROBOTS WITHOUT A CARE IN THE WORLD.

EH... BEEP?

BEEP.

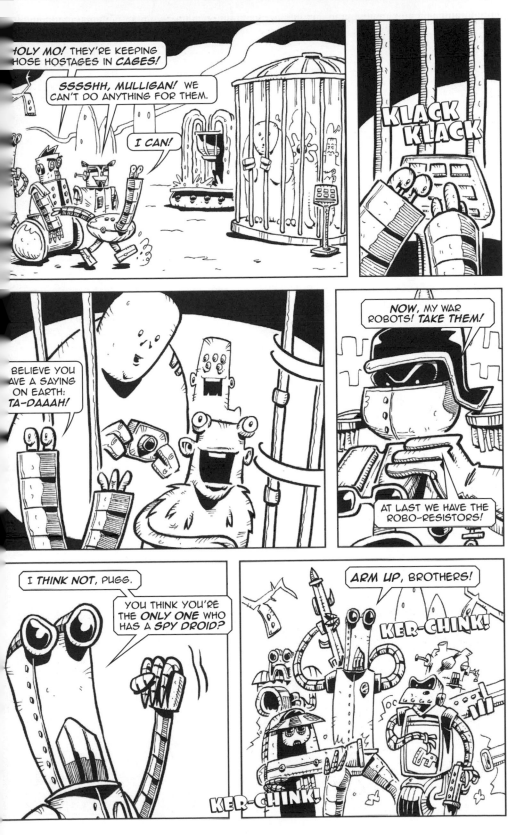

32

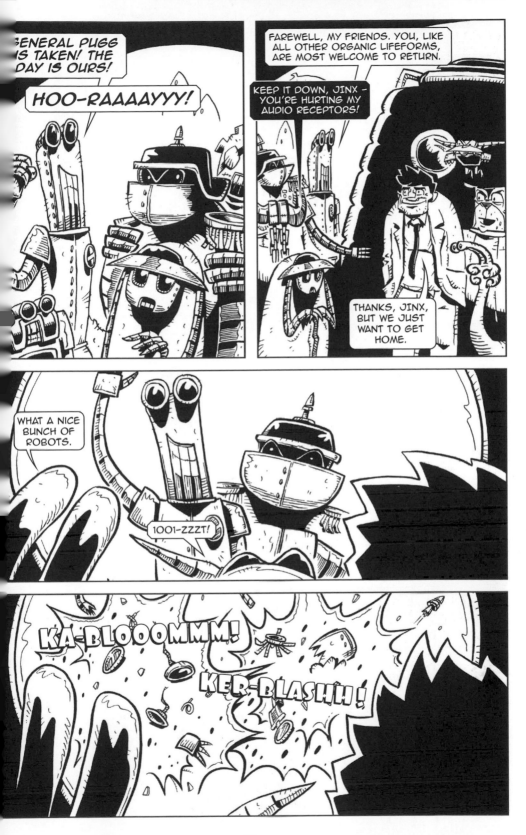

vega

Vega, in the Argon Reservation, was designated a class 4 gambling planet in 17299.

This many-mooned planet is entirely owned and operated by the Puzo Pleasure Pursuits Corporation, a galaxy-spanning company known for aggressively protecting their interests.

This means that on Vega, gamblers who lose and can't pay may end up losing more than they bargain for.

The inhabitants of Vega are all addicted to gambling and bet and take bets as a matter of course on every single activity they do, whether it is a game of eye-spy or simply who wakes up first in the house in the morning.

The surface of the planet is covered in casinos, bam bam race courses and sports arenas.

vega   THE HOME OF BAM BAM rACING

A popular sport throughout the galaxy, the first ever bam bam race was held on Vega in 17320. Legendary champion jockey Jenna Drax on her mount Thelonius III successfully completed the course, jumping the treacherous Beeble's Brook and eliminated 90% of her fellow jockeys with pinpoint accuracy using her trademark weapon of choice, the Laz-inator 4000.

visit:

Hope Springs – a natural hot spring where the lucky and unlucky alike relax after a hard day at the Vega casino's gronk tables.

eat at:

Chancer's Eats – where diners take bets on which mystery dishes they are served.

grade:

THERE'S AN *INVISIBLE, ODOURLESS GAS* COMING OUT OF THE VENT!

RUNT RECKONS IT'S PACKED WITH *NEURO-TOXINS* AND IT'S FLOODING THE WHOLE OF VEGA'S ATMOSPHERE – WE'RE *BREATHING* IT RIGHT NOW!

A *GAMBLING GAS?* MAYBE THAT'S WHAT HAS SENT EVERYONE HERE *BETTING BANANAS!* IT'S EVEN STARTING TO *AFFECT US!*

THAT MUST BE WHAT THE *PUZO CORPORATION* ARE UP TO – GASSING THE POPULATION SO THEY *KEEP ON GAMBLING!*

AND KEEP ON SWELLING THE PUZO CORP COFFERS!

I'VE AN IDEA—

IN MY BOOK, *MILKY WAY MEMOIRS* —

OH, BROTHER...

— THE HERO HAD TO MAKE HIS WAY THROUGH A POISON GAS MINEFIELD!

AND HOW DID HE DO THAT?

ALL·SPECIES SCUBA·WEAR

'E *BET* YOU'LL LOVE IT!

IT'S *EASY* IF YOU'VE GOT THE *RIGHT EQUIPMENT!*

PHEW! THIS *BREATHING APPARATUS* ACTUALLY *WORKS!*

SUDDENLY I DON'T WANT TO BET ON—

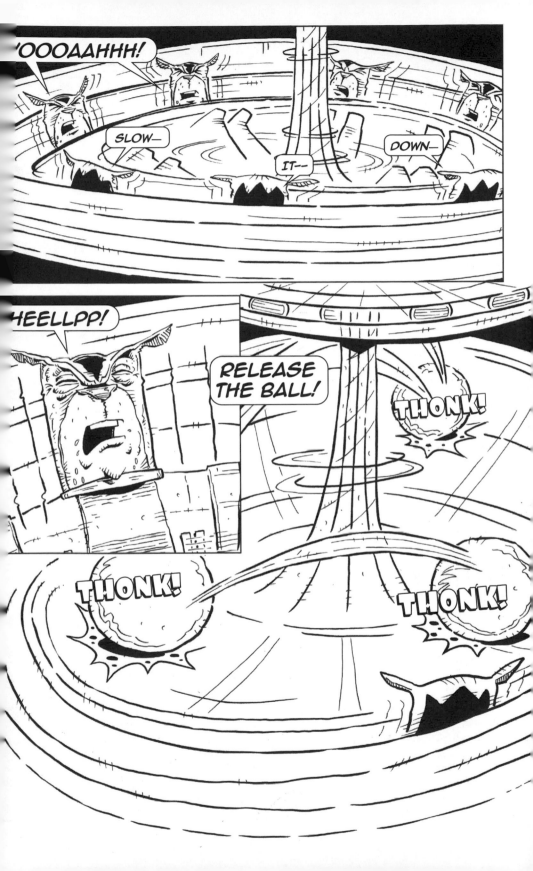

44

AZUR

Azur holds the distinction of being the only planet in the galaxy to be made almost completely of pure water.

Over the millennia, asteroids splashed into the planet's liquid surface and were caught within in its gravity field, becoming floating continents.

Aquatic life living in the water began to populate the rocks, becoming amphibious and sentient, eventually evolving into the Azurians.

Azurians are green skinned aliens with rubbery hands for heads, and an arm on their 'tail'. They communicate by clicking their face fingers in a kind of sign language. They can breath air, and have gills to allow them to also breath water.

The Azurians are a very religious race who worship water, and the pure water planet is under constant attack from 'water pirates' – aliens intent on stealing the water itself, one the galaxy's most scarce commodities.

However, as many potential raiders have found, the planet is very well defended by warrior priests, who, as well as looking after their flocks, fight off incursions by pirate raiding parties.

water pirates

The pirates that plague Azur are made up mostly of the vicious Ban-Tam race from the nearby planet of Koop. The most notorious of these is Captain Silkie who has conducted over 300 successful water raids on Azur.

●━━━━● captain silkie

Silkie commands a crew of fifteen Ban-Tams on his space-galleon 'The Water Fowl'.

Water pirates' galleons are typically powered by solar sails which take their energy from nearby suns, and are usually armed with lazer-cannons and heat-ray harpoons.

● a water
pirate galleon
(WATER BUCKET NOT PICTURED)

visit:

Rock 3, Azur's largest asteroid continent, renowned for the beauty of its mysterious underground cathedrals.

eat at:

Red Snapper's - the snurk pie is first class!

grade:

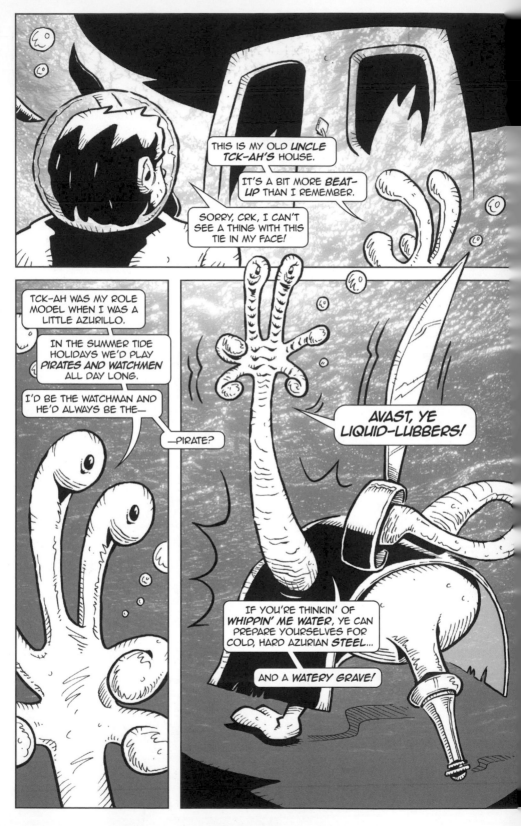

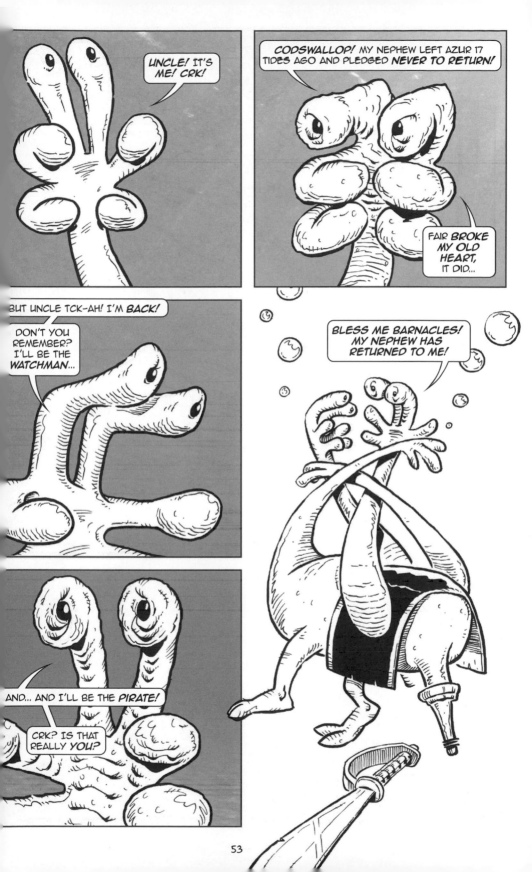

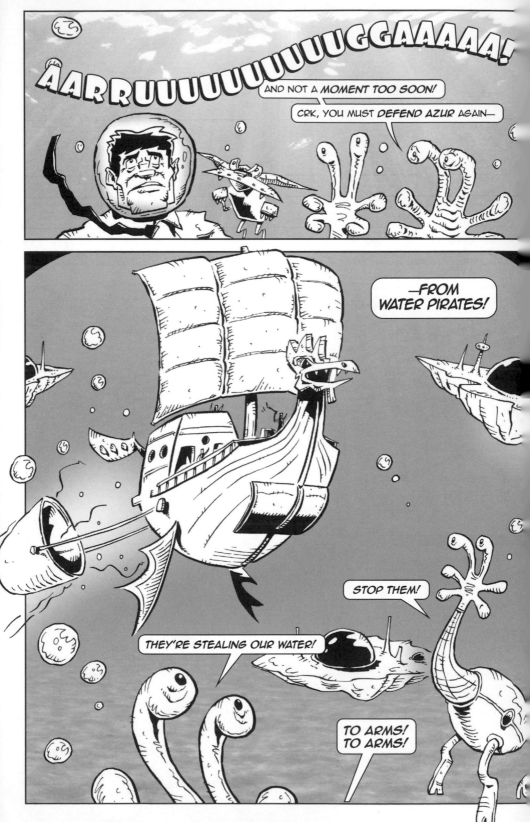

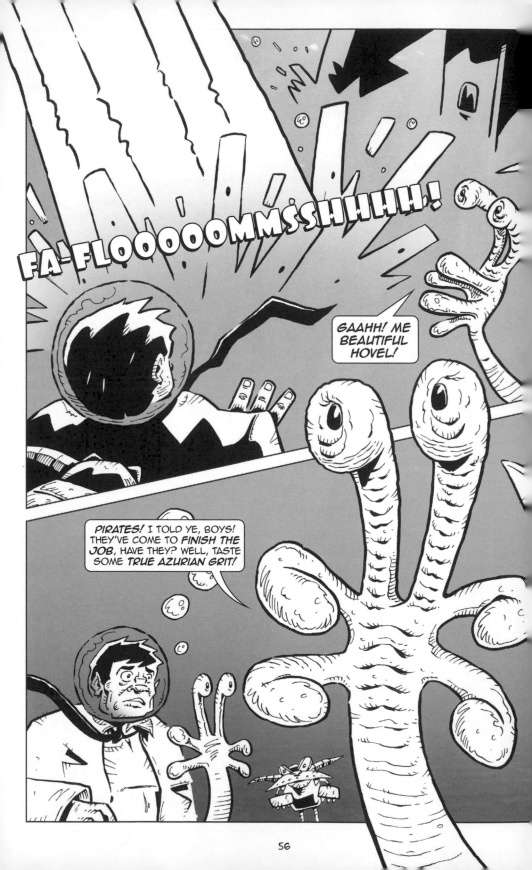

58

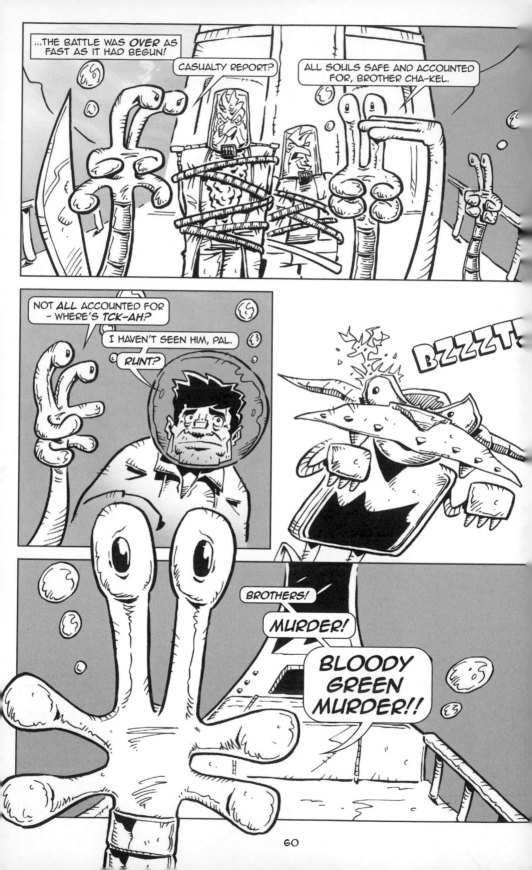

61

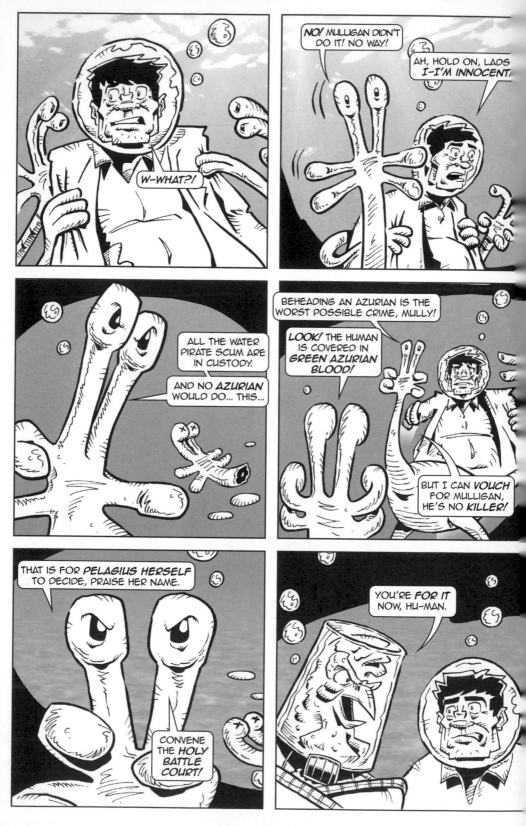

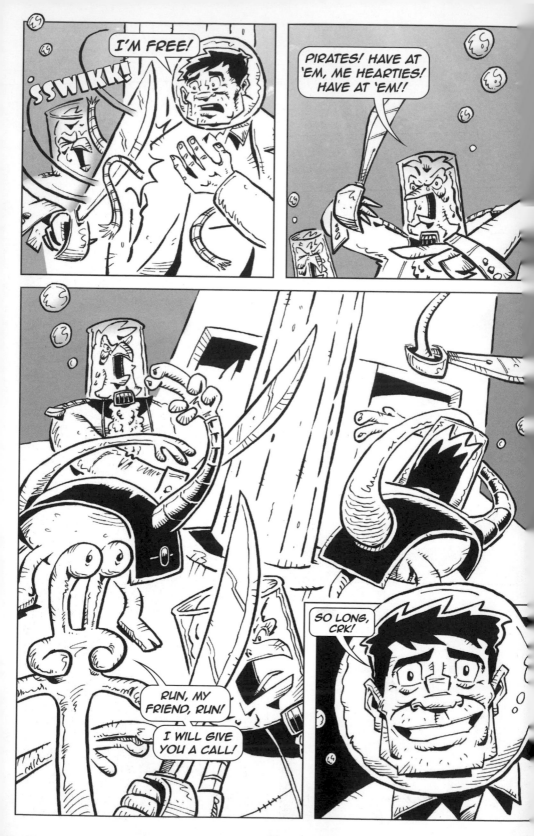

earth

This little known planet is situated in the Gamma Quadrant.

Its inhabitants, the humans, are a semi-evolved, war-like species who seem content to fight amongst themselves, probably because they are not yet clever enough to have effectively mastered space flight.

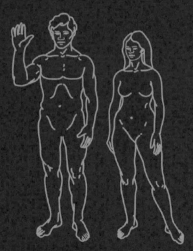

Despite this, they have as of this date managed to get to their own moon, and have sent probes to planets within their solar system.

One such probe caused a small panic on Jupiter when it disrupted their bi-annual solar surfing championships, crossing the path of the contestants and knocking the reigning champion, Jools 'Quicksilver' Vectron, off his board and costing him the platinum medal.

fancy a laugh?

Read **Milky Way Memoirs** by human Marion Mulligan, a book so riddled with basic factual errors about our glorious galaxy, it would bring a smile to the face of a depressed Telosian.

eat at:

Earth cuisine is pretty unpalatable - we advise getting drive-through at the excellent Numbo's on nearby Venus.

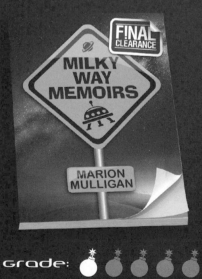

grade:

ZEEBO WAS **WEAK**.

HIS **GAMBLING** WAS PUTTING MY MASTER IN BZZT **DANGER**.

I **MIS-TRANSLATED** HONEST VIGG'S OFFER TO LET HIM GO IF HE GAVE HIM THE **LOTTERY CARD**.

ZEEBO HEARD VIGG SAY THAT HE WOULD LET HIM GO IF **ZEEBO AND YOU** WERE TO **EXCHANGE PLACES**.

ZEEBO **REFUSED**.

NOW ZEEBO IS **NO LONGER** A ZZZT **DANGER** TO MY MASTER.

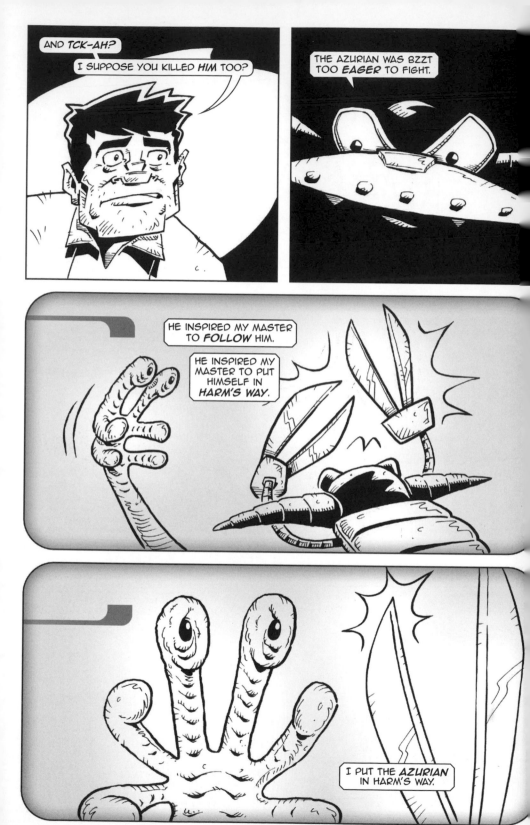

U MURDERING BUCKET OF DIODES!

YOU'RE MEANT TO BE A *TRANSLATOR*, NOT AN *AVENGING ANGEL OF DEATH!!*

MERE!

RUNT DID IT FOR ZZZZTTT YOUR *OWN GOOD*, MASTER ZZZTTTT MULLIGAN!

RABBED HIM. WAS SO LIGHT.

O11OO1110! *ZZZT!*

IT WAS THEN THAT I NOTICED THE *SCORCH MARKS* ON RUNT'S HEAD.

FUNNY THING. NEVER *NOTICED* THEM BEFORE.

I CAN'T BLAME MYSELF, THOUGH. HOW OFTEN DO YOU LOOK AT THE BACK OF A WASHING MACHINE FOR SIGNS OF DAMAGE?

OR THE UNDERSIDE OF A TOASTER?

I THINK WHEN BRINNER HIT HIM WITH THAT *LAZER BOLT* WAY BACK IN FLOTSAM CITY, IT DID MORE DAMAGE THAN WE THOUGHT.

IT MUST HAVE *SCREWED UP* HIS PROGAMMING.

...TURNED HIM FROM A SIMPLE *TRANSLATOR DEVICE* INTO A *TWISTED, BLOOD THIRSTY BODYGUARD!*

uploading file.
saving file.
new file: mulligan.exe
complete.

...AND THAT'S HOW I ENDED UP HERE. BACK IN DARLIN' OLD DUBLIN.

I MADE RUNT *FLY BACK TO EARTH*, YOU SEE.

HE USED UP THE LAST OF HIS POWER DOING IT.

WELL, IT DIDN'T TAKE TOO LONG, AND WITH HIS *ENCYCLOPAEDIC* KNOWLEDGE OF EARTH IT WAS EASY FOR HIM TO ENTER THE ATMOSPHERE AT *JUST THE RIGHT SPEED* AND TRAJECTORY TO SPLASH DOWN RIGHT IN THE *CENTRE OF THE CITY.*

THE *DEAD CENTRE*, AT 370 KMPH. YOU CAN SAY A LOT OF THINGS ABOUT RUNT, BUT YOU CAN'T FAULT HIS *AIM*...

YOU SEE, RUNT SAVED *ME,* BUT HE DIDN'T SAVE *MY LIFE.*

HE UPLOADED *MY BRAIN,* MY THOUGHTS AND MEMORIES – MY *SELF* – INTO HIS DATA BANKS.

AND THAT'S WHERE
I AM NOW.

...BACK HOME IN DUBLIN...

incoming call

EH.

HELLO?

caller i.d. crk-tish-crrrkkk

MULLIGAN?
IT'S *CRK!*

JUST CALLING TO
SEE IF YOU *NEED*
A HAND?

mulligan, marion

CRK, ME OUL FLOWER!

*IT'S GREAT TO
HEAR FROM YOU!*

FUNNY YOU SHOULD
MENTION IT...

mulligan, marion

SOMETIMES HELP COMES ALONG
WHEN YOU LEAST EXPECT IT.

HEH. GOOD OLD *CRK*. RIDING TO THE
RESCUE, JUST LIKE IN A STORY.

YOU KNOW, MAYBE IT'S TIME TO GET
MYSELF A NICE NEW *CLONE BODY*,
TO STOP RABBITIN' ON ABOUT
MILKY WAY MEMOIRS...

...AND TO START WORKING
ON A SEQUEL...?

*Original sketches for various bad guys,
vagabonds and ne'er-do-wells.*

Alan Nolan lives and works in Bray, County Wicklow, Ireland. He is co-creator (with Ian Whelan) of SANCHO comic, which was shortlisted for two Eagle awards, and is writer and illustrator of the SKREWY SCIENCE WITH PROF. BUTTERKNUT & KRONK cartoon strip for the *Irish Times*. He is the author and illustrator of *The Big Break Detectives Casebook* and the 'Murder Can Be Fatal' series (The O'Brien Press).

Special thanks to Helen, Michael, Emma, Ivan and all at The O'Brien Press,
and to my long-suffering family – Rachel, Adam, Matthew and Sam.

www.murdercanbefatal.com

www.alannolan.ie